공주와 완두콩

The Princess and the Pea

원작 안데르센 글 한정림

감수 Jeffrey S. Zeter 그림 이은선

삼성출판사
samsungbooks.com

There is a prince.
He is very handsome.
But he is very sad, too.

4

He wants to find a princess.
There are many princesses.
But he wants a real princess.

One night, there is a storm.
The thunder is very loud.
The lightning is very bright.

9

Then there is a knock on the door.
The two big doors open.
Outside, there is a wet princess.

She says, "Oh, my!
I am so wet. I am tired, too.
May I rest in the castle
this evening?"

"Wow! She is beautiful!" the prince says.
"Yes, but is she a real princess?" the queen says.
"Hmm ... I don't know," the prince says.

"I am so sleepy," says the princess.
"But I can only sleep on a very comfortable bed.
Please prepare a soft, smooth,
comfortable bed for me."

The queen listens to the princess.
Then she has a good idea.

"Don't worry, son," she says.
"We will discover
if she is a real princess!"
And she has one small pea.

17

The queen puts the pea on the bed.
Then her maids put ten soft mattresses down.
Then they put nine very soft mattresses down.
Then they put eight feather mattresses down.
Then they put seven soft blankets down.

"OK, dear!" says the queen.
"Time for bed!"

21

At breakfast, the princess is very tired.
"Are you tired?" asks the queen.

"Yes, I am very tired!" says the princess.
"There is a big rock in my bed!
Oh! My back hurts! Ouch!"

The queen is very happy!
Only a real princess
could feel the pea.
The queen knows this.
'She is a real princess!'
thinks the prince.

So the prince and the princess are married.
They are very happy.

And where is the pea?
It might be in your bed.

This is the **princess.**
This is the **pea.**
Shooby dooby dooby
Dooby dooby dee

The **princess** and the **pea**
The **princess** and the **pea**
Shooby dooby dooby
Dooby dooby dee

작사 한정림 작곡 이숙현

This is the princess. This is the pea.　Shooby dooby dooby　Dooby dooby dee　The

prin - cess and the pea The princess and the pea　Shooby dooby dooby　Dooby dooby dee

What it means...

p.4

한 왕자가 있었어요.
왕자는 아주 멋있었어요.
하지만 왕자는 매우 슬펐어요.

p.7

왕자는 공주를 찾고 싶어해요.
공주들은 많이 있었어요.
하지만 왕자는 진정한 공주를 원했던 거예요.

p.8

어느 날 밤, 폭풍우가 몰아쳤어요.
천둥이 매우 크게 쳤고요.
번개가 매우 환하게 내리쳤어요.

p.11

그때, 문 두드리는 소리가 났어요.
커다란 두 문이 열렸어요.
밖에는 비에 흠뻑 젖은 공주가 서 있었어요.

p.12

공주가 말했어요.
"아! 저는 흠뻑 젖었어요. 피곤하기도 하고요.
오늘 밤 이 성에서 쉬어 가도 될까요?"

"와! 그녀는 아름다워요!"
왕자가 말했어요.
　　"그래, 하지만 그녀가 진정한 공주일까?"
여왕이 말했어요.
　　"흠······, 모르겠어요." 왕자가 대답했죠.

p.14

"아함! 너무 졸려요."
공주가 말했어요.
"그렇지만, 저는 아주 편안한 침대에서만
잠을 잘 수 있어요.
저를 위해 아주 부드럽고 편편하고 편안한
침대를 준비해 주세요."
공주가 덧붙였어요.

p.16

여왕은 공주의 말을 들었어요.
곧 좋은 생각이 떠올랐지요.

p.17

"걱정하지 마라, 아들아."
여왕이 말했어요.
"그녀가 진정한 공주인지 아닌지
알게 될 거다."
그리고 작은 완두콩을 한 알 갖고 왔지요.

p.18

여왕은 침대 위에 완두콩을 놓았어요.
그 위에 하녀들이 부드러운 요를 열 개 깔았어요.
그 위에 아주 부드러운 요를 아홉 개 깔았어요.
그리고 그 위에 깃털로 만든 요를
여덟 개 깔았지요.
그리고 부드러운 담요를 일곱 개 깔았어요.

p.21

"좋아요, 공주님!"
여왕이 말했어요.
"자, 이제 잘 시간이에요!"